Shorty ♡
wing Wong

by the same author
THE GIRO PLAYBOY

Shorty Loves Wing Wong

+ other small town sketches

Michael Smith +
Jim Medway

ff

faber and faber

First published in 2006
by Paul Stolper and To Hell
to coincide with an exhibition of the original drawings
at the Paul Stolper Gallery

This edition first published in 2007
by Faber and Faber Limited
3 Queen Square London WC1N 3AU

Typeset by Faber & Faber Limited
Printed in England by Mackays of Chatham plc,
Chatham, Kent

The illustrator gratefully acknowledges the support of
the Arts Council

A CIP record for this book
is available from the British Library

ISBN 978-0-571-23471-4

2 4 6 8 10 9 7 5 3 1

For the first time in years I was back on the Headland, and being back on the Headland was priceless . . . the quietness and the quaintness and the seagulls following the fishing boats into the safety of the harbour . . . the town settling down after another slow day, just as it has done forever . . . the Headland is the best bit, the mediaeval fishing village that was eclipsed by the dirty industrial port over the bay in Victorian times . . . the Headland is where I grew up and haven't been back to for more than a car ride in at least seven years . . . the place I saw first, the place I was formed by, the place where I was now both a long-lost son and in many ways a stranger to . . .

My first night back, sat in the drunken glow of the Albatross pub, and the company of old pals and the locals felt like the long-lost truth I'd spent the last ten years trying to brush aside . . . I never went in the Albatross when I was younger, I'd heard too many stories about the cat fights with women trying to gouge each other's eyes out with their white stilettos, and as a sensitive teenage longhair type I wouldn't have set foot in there for a million quid, but being here now it didn't seem that rough . . . we got chatting to a couple of fishermen who were boozing it up after five weeks out on the boats . . . their approach to life was very raw and robust, shall we say, but once I'd told them I'd grown up round the corner and we worked out that they vaguely knew my dad, it was all hunky-dory, and when I told them I was writing stories about the Headland they got into it, especially Big Tony, on the proviso that, 'You get me a tinny in, mush,

seeing as you're diggin' into me napper' . . . I got him a
tinny in, he talked, and I laughed and listened . . . it turned
out he'd been a pal of David Wise, my dad's old drinking
buddy, a photographer who'd passed away and seemed to
have drunk with people wherever I go, from drinking
clubs in Soho to fishermen's pubs on the Headland to our
house with my dad when I was only just old enough to
remember, and so my life comes back full circle
somehow . . . and the stories began to unravel like the
tides and currents the fish follow, with them lot following
the fish on their rickety little boats all round the globe,
'Halfway to the fucking Falkland Islands, kidder,' and they
know all the flows of the ocean because it's their lives, or
at least that's how it seemed to me and how I wanted it to
be, like some macho romantic Hemingway story . . . they
were intense stories, raw stories, as raw as anyone's life
ever was, but I have to be careful now because Big Tony
said if I stitched him up in any way or slated the
Headland, 'I'll come and find you down London and cut
your bollocks off, bonny lad.' I'm very fond of my
bollocks and to be honest I haven't got bollocks big
enough to test that statement out, so I won't tell you any
of those stories. Except the skate story.

Skate are big fish, flat things with wings the size of a pub table, and he was telling us about the time they caught a huge one, the size of a single bed . . . its neck was as broad as a tree, and when you cut skates' heads off their big thick spinal cords are ringed like a tree trunk, ringed with the history of their long lives . . . 'That fucker was at least seventy years old,' he reckoned – a freak . . . apparently you get lots of freaky mutant fish coming up out of the sea, especially these days with all the pollution . . . 'slinky' they call them, fat misshapen things with weird organs spilling out when you run a knife through them . . . they dredge up lots of slinky as well as strange unknown species they're discovering all the time, especially up in the north of Scotland where the seabed falls off into the depths of the mid-Atlantic shelf, and ancient abominations occasionally come up from the deep . . . the skate sounded freaky enough though, and I asked him jokingly if you could fuck 'em, because according to my friends from Grimsby that's what their lot used to do with halibut . . . this had my boys laughing and Tony relished in it, telling us how if you get your fingers up a lady skate, its sad dead-looking mouth turns up at the corners like it's smiling and it tries to wrap its fins around you . . . my mates were in stitches and the faces on their women would have turned milk sour . . . 'It must get awfully lonely out on them boats, like, Tony . . .' I joked playfully, half expecting him to cut my bollocks off there and then, but I was relieved to see that he kept laughing along too.

Walking round the seafront, the sea all silvery-
grey and still on a mildly cloudy, nothing kind
of day, the Cleveland Hills rolling along gently
on the other side of the bay, punctuated by the steelworks
and its plume of smoke reminiscent of the mushroom
cloud, beautiful in its own way . . . seeing how quiet it all
is, how there's really nothing going on at all, a simple kind
of place that doesn't ask for much, and doesn't get much
back in return . . . but it is beautiful, beautiful and restful
and still, if that's what you want . . . it wasn't what I
wanted, and I was off the first chance I got . . . looking at
the place now, trying to remember what we found to do,
I suppose we just made our own fun . . . I walked past that
concrete bunker with the curvy roof we'd sit on top of all
night in the summer . . . you could only get to it by a risky
jump off the town wall, and it was like our own special
place no one else could reach, and I loved whiling away
the long evenings looking out across the bay at night and
the people walking past us below like we were invisible
and the curvy concrete roof was a magic carpet taking us
to our own secret enchanted world or something . . .

Our favourite secret special place was the tarzie rope up Steetley . . . Steetley was a huge, foreboding chemical plant that produced industrial magnesium, with a massive tower spreading a slow brown cloud over the surrounding housing estates and a very long and tall pier that pumped all the waste products out into the North Sea . . . the pier had a tarzie rope attached off a pipe at about the height of two double-decker buses, and you'd climb maybe about a third of the way up the rusty leg and take a run along a wooden beam and jump, and the next thing you knew you'd be swinging over the beach in this huge arc going so hard you'd get a tingling feeling in your pelvic cavity and it really was a thrill . . . you just had to be careful when you jumped you didn't fall into the leak from the little pipe that flowed down to the shore and congealed on the way into this horrible spunky foam stuff that was almost directly in your landing path . . .

We used to spend whole days wandering up to Steetley, which was a bit further along the coast and dangerously close to Geordieland and the coal fields of County Durham . . . the Pit Yakkers made Hartle-pudlians look posh and the kids you'd run into on the beach up there were all horrible glue-sniffing desperadoes, kids with no chance, kids who didn't know wrong from right, kids we'd do our best to stay away from . . . the coal from the pit villages found its way back on to the beach and the maritime beauty was blighted by waves of black coal washed up against the beach in successive dirty tidemarks . . . the 'coal wallers' would scour the beach collecting sacks of the stuff and sell it on to people like my mam who still had a real coal fire, though burning coal was illegal because of its high sulphur content . . . I remember one of my jobs was sitting in the back yard painstakingly picking all the seaweed and centipedes out of the 'sea coal' ready for the fire . . . it was a dirty job but it paid handsomely at two quid an hour . . .

It did used to get a bit boring sometimes and I remember on the first day of our Easter holiday an early case of adolescent ennui creeping in, thinking just how on earth we were going to fill up the time, when we found a box of 20 Regal King Size, unopened, still with the plastic wrapper on, lying on the sand . . . we went to the shop for some matches – and bingo! I remember the taste of that first fag, so pungent and complex; I remember it burning the back of my throat out like inhaling the smoke from a bonfire; I remember coming over all dizzy and I remember being fantastically excited at the prospect of the adult thrills opening out to me that night on the beach . . . I went home later and in the privacy of my bedroom I had the distinct sensation that my balls dropped. I've never really known if your 'balls dropping' was an old wives' tale or not but it was a strange new sensation, and as I sat on my bed perplexed and excited I felt an enormous sense of what was to come.

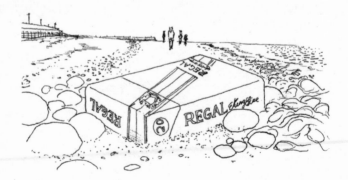

That holiday was a naughty one. A day or two later we sent Dingo to the corner shop to get a cigar because he was taller and looked about fifteen or sixteen, whereas we all looked about thirteen or fourteen, which we were . . . we went to the beach and smoked it, inhaling it, but it wasn't much improvement on the fags really . . . we needed something harder . . . next we made a trek over the other side of town, to Seaton, Hartlepool's rather half-arsed attempt at a kiss-me-quick resort, where we knew there was an offy that was run by a senile half-blind old biddy who would serve young people drink . . . off went Dingo, who came back with a carrier bag full of Newcastle Brown, and then we headed off down the arcades, power drinking it all behind the bus shelter . . . suddenly I was drunk . . . the thing that really struck me about being drunk was I realised I couldn't stop being drunk; I had no control over the situation and was completely debilitated and at the mercy of a chemical in my bloodstream . . . I'd always presumed you were the same really and the drink enabled you to be merry but you were still kind of sober if you wanted to be; seeing the all-powerful effect something as prosaic as Newcastle Brown could have on the mind and body led to a profound realisation about the nature of my own mortality; I'd always thought I could live till I was three hundred and fifty if I just put my mind to it, that everything was in the mind, but now I understood I was subject to immutable laws and all those superhuman things just weren't going to happen . . . so I smashed the bottles against the bus shelter and went

off to the arcades ... once I got there I needed a piss so I went back behind the bus shelter ... once I got back to the arcades I needed a piss again so off I went back to the bus shelter ... and so it went on and on for ages, in between shouting insulting stuff at the little Seaton tarts we fancied who were hanging around the arcades ... maybe this is Dutch courage, I thought ... maybe this is what it feels like to be a man ...

Next up we got a canister of gas and went down the beach with it ... It had a strange cold taste to it and it made me go dizzy in a way I didn't like ... I felt my chest go a bit funny and I'd heard it could kill you by making your lungs seize up, so we took it to a slag heap near Steetley, threw a huge rock and a match at it and watched it go up in a spectacular fireball ...

So that was how we had our fun, whiling away the long days of summer, walking for miles up the dirty beach, Joe singing his silly songs about pubes on his genitals and Walshy taking his finger out of his belly button and asking you to smell it, and for some reason it stinking of arses, and us all laughing, not knowing it would soon all change and be gone for good, with us all going our separate ways and growing into different people . . .

Of that gang, a few turned into real wrong 'uns . . . Dingo and Doyle graduated into pouring paraffin down rabbit holes and blowing them up, and when the rabbits came flying out, they'd get them and stick twigs through their ears and into their brains . . . Doyle was a right toerag, a kid with the palest, sickliest complexion in the world . . . my abiding image of him is him eating his appalling daily lunch of five bags of pickled onion Space Raiders, the famous 10p corn snacks. As a kid Dingo was very funny, but once he hit puberty he became spotty and cruel, and full of rage . . . I remember the first inklings of this when he became obsessed with Iron Maiden and zombie movies, and then that day we went to Walton's pet shop and he bought a bag of goldfish, took them to the beck round the back of the school and stabbed the bag in a penknife frenzy until it was full of holes gushing water that had turned into an orange golden mess with little bits of fish floating about . . . it horrified me, wasn't fun any more, and we didn't hang out much longer . . .

So anyway, **they** went their way and I went mine, the fast track towards bongs, acid, growing my hair long and listening to my dad's old Beatles albums . . . I was very quickly immersed in a Strawberry Fields-style inner world that seemed completely at odds with the outer one . . . I was seeing crocodiles coming out of walls before I'd even lost my virginity . . . there was a girl I knew who got it too who wore one of those horrible hippy skirts with little mirrors sewn in who was also going through her dad's Beatles collection . . . we hung out a lot and did our first trips together, sitting on the seafront thinking the horizon was a giant velvet-curtained theatre etc, and we were just friends until one night when she said, 'I'll kiss you if you want,' and that was that . . . I was smitten from then on and found it too hard to do anything about it because I felt cripplingly shy and unable to deal with the tumult of new emotion . . . I left it a bit too long and she got it on with Gary, the smooth-talking older lad who played bass in a band, the bastard . . .

By this time we'd moved into a huge, draughty, dilapidated old house ... It was spooky and strange and I reckoned it was haunted by the ghost of old Bob Mason the printer ... my mam and dad both told me not to be silly as a kid, but recently she admitted to seeing a girl in a Victorian dress coming slowly up the stairs, and he admitted that the noise of children's feet running across the landing wasn't in fact the noise of the water pipes ... it didn't help being constantly stoned on my own in the weird room nobody liked and I could never get rid of the feeling I was being watched ... I don't really have fond memories of that old house and when I walked past it, looking through the windows was like looking through a shadowy lens into a memory from a sinister dream, and the house troubled me like a skeleton in a closet that still made the doors creak when it tried to get out at night ...

By now I had hair like Ian Brown and some vintage '70s Levis I'd wear with a pair of maroon Converse . . . I looked pretty cool come to think of it, but my mind was shot, having sunk into a permanent low-grade jittery cannabis psychosis . . . I had very few people I could talk to who didn't spin me out and felt deathly depressed most of the time . . . I think that phase can be quite neatly compartmentalised as the 'full-blown teenager' phase . . . I did get a bird though, a cute little redhead who looked like Tanya Donelly out of the Throwing Muses . . . she popped my cherry straddled on top of me one afternoon when my parents were out, and after that lots of the things that seemed wrong with the world looked far more simple and harmonious again.

One day I got on the number 7 bus and went to the Burn Valley. The Burn Valley was another special place to me . . . walking down the winding steps into it now, 'School is shit', 'Joel is lush' and 'Shorty loves Wing Wong' graffitied on the wall . . . I suppose some things never change . . . I wonder if some sensitive long-haired lad is sat down there on the Fairy Steps smoking dope and is going to be asked to give a mirror-skirted hippy girl a kiss soon, and go insane with the flutter of adolescent hormones . . .

BURN VALLEY GARDENS
☼CLOSING TIMES☙

APRIL	9.00pm
MAY	9.30pm
JUNE	10.00pm
JULY	10.00pm
AUGUST	9.30pm
SEPTEMBER	8.30pm
OCTOBER	6.30pm
NOVEMBER	4.30pm
DECEMBER	4.30pm
JANUARY	4.30pm
FEBRUARY	5.00pm
MARCH	7.00pm

OR DUSK IF EARLIER

[handwritten over the notice: "I Shagged Colette Lacy in here last night twice"]

I discovered the Burn Valley at the same time as our Steetley adventures, on the cusp of adolescence, a beautiful Indian summer of childhood when the world seemed to be opening out into a wider movie called adult life and it felt so exciting to be entering that independent exploratory phase with it all laid out ahead of me . . . our school was in the middle of a shitty grey council estate and when we used to sneak out at dinnertime to the local shops it was always full of Dobermans, horrible mams feeding kids pasties and really nasty delinquents with names like 'Flogger' or 'Buzzard' doing glue and smashing bottles . . . Discovering the Burn Valley was discovering a new country, a magic idyll of peace and green rolling down to a shady brook . . . we weren't allowed out of school at lunchtime, and we seemed to be the only kids who even knew about the place, which only added to the sense of exploring a new frontier . . . the pot of gold at the end of the rainbow was the chippy on Elwick Road, which was superb, miles ahead of the soggy tasteless muck they served up at the local shops, and besides, I kind of fancied the woman behind the counter, which was odd because she was around forty, but she had a lovely way about her, and when she beamed you a smile she had the most beautiful perfect teeth, which thinking about it now she'd obviously had done up . . . then there was also the fact there were the birds from Tunny, the school for the rich kids who lived behind the park – the Tunny lasses were always fitter somehow, better turned out, Mediterranean-looking even, just the way I've always liked them . . .

The Burn Valley was also the location of Brinkburn sixth-form college, and walking to the chippy you'd see kids in big jeans and weird hair going on about bands . . . It seemed like the coolest place in the world to me and when everyone else went on to our sixth form at school where I don't think you were even allowed to wear jeans (though maybe I'm remembering that bit wrong), I decided to break with tradition and head to the bright lights of Brinkburn like it was Manhattan or somewhere . . .

I spent most of my sixth-form career sat down the Fairy Steps, skinning up instead of going to class, so stoned I was no use to anyone, including myself . . . I couldn't understand why I felt compelled to sabotage my life like this and still don't . . . one day we were at the Fairy Steps after going down the town for lunch . . . I'd bought these daft stripy pyjama-bottom things for a quid in the market, and everyone taunted me that I couldn't walk around wearing them, so just to show them I put them on and took my top off and my shoes and socks as well . . . the fact I had a skinhead at the time must've added to the effect; I looked like someone on day release and even the Floggers and Buzzards of this world didn't give me any lip as we walked back to the Burny from town . . . once we got back, for my pièce de résistance, I took a big run and jumped the beck; no one ever had the balls to jump the beck; looking at it now, it's quite a stretch, with a sharp concrete drop on either side . . . I'd always wanted to jump the beck, but was always too chickenshit, and only now I'd stepped outside the normal constraints, freed myself, bare-chested and bare-footed with Ali Baba pants on, like some Nietzschean überman, did I believe completely I could do it . . . I certainly showed all them cowardly fuckers who the daddy was that day.

Before I headed back to the Smoke I went down the town and met my granny and granda at the Grand Hotel . . . The Grand Hotel is a stately Edwardian affair whose glory days are long gone, but when you see all the old folks in the front gossiping over their cream teas you get a whiff of an old kind of elegance and maybe even glamour . . . I met them inside and they'd come to see me in their Sunday best, looking proud as punch . . . a table of my grandma's whist buddies were in and I was shown off, introduced as our Anne's son who lives down London and has written a novel . . . since I got the book deal they look at me as a writer, though I've been a writer a lot longer, but I'm not complaining; it's nice to see the sparkle in their eyes . . . now I'm the writer their eyes light up and they want to tell me all their stories about the Old Town, the port bit where they grew up that was always flooding and got razed to the ground before I was born and eventually became the shiny new marina, complete with fake Georgian quay and discount factory outlets . . . the stories always come back to the pub my granda grew up in, the pub and its characters – stories about Ducky Merryweather, Hartlepool's first puff; Fishy Annie, a huge woman who used to walk round town selling fish in a pram; Charlie Buzzer, the strange chap who walked the streets with his trousers tied up with string who made buzzing and whirring noises instead of speaking, and Eddie the Murderer, the club singer who always wore spats and once killed a cat, dried it out and then put it through a mangle . . . the conversation was rolling till my granda's cousin came in and sat with us,

followed by an impressive lady like an eighty-year-old Marilyn Monroe, but with her hair dyed too brightly and her jewellery a little overdone . . . my grandma's face dropped and she suddenly came up with excuses and ushered me and my granda out . . . it all came out on the steps: 'I'm not having a drink in the Grand Hotel with a bloody hooer! What the hell's your Teddy doing going out with her, John? I tell you, our Mike, in her day she was the biggest bloody hooer in the town!' 'Aye, and the prettiest as well,' my granda added, which started a delightful little row; he insisted she was prettier than all the film stars when she was young, and I had to agree, she certainly would've been a looker; 'Ooh, she was beautiful.' 'Aye, but in a rough kind of way,' my grandma had to get in; undeterred, my granda carried on, 'You know the expression Salt of the Earth? Well, that was her; she'd always help people out with a bob or two when there was no work; she always had a spare bob or two like, because she was the priciest; when the boats came in you'd see them all lined up, sat against the wall with one leg crossed, and they'd have their price written on the sole of their shoe . . .' and as he told me the rest he got increasingly impish and my granny got increasingly sour-faced; and as they quarrelled about the prettiest hooer in the town they became younger somehow, and I saw their youth, the era of matinée idols and the Grand Hotel being quite the place, saw the young guy and his girl coming through the wrinkles and the Sunday best . . .

My **last evening,** taking a final walk round the place before heading back to the Smoke . . . quietly conquered by the beauty of the Tees Bay, the evening sky shot through with red like the ancient of days to which we all eventually return . . . packing up my stuff in my friend's house a few doors along from 24 McDonald Place, the two-up two-down all my earliest memories are from, memories of riding round on a tricycle or dressing up with a plastic helmet and sword claiming to be 'The Roman Greek' . . . my

friend never grew up on the Headland, but moved here a year ago after being away for a while, like Joanne did, my old flame who made me happiest and most hurt, who's now bringing up a baby a few doors down; like my dad did too, turning up with a wife and two young kids in tow, and it's strange and somehow comforting to think that if my dad's time had been a generation later I'm sure he'd've known Kirsty and Andy Kelly, my pals over here leading lives that are probably pretty similar to his, and they'd maybe all have drunk in the Albatross together, and one day I might even have gone round his house with Kirsty or Kelly and talked to his young boy not quite old enough to remember, just like David Wise had with me ... we go through life thinking we are making our own decisions in isolation, rarely glimpsing that we are all part of a wider process, a process that fulfils itself through us over time and the generations ... and as I pack my bags all these things are joining up together in my mind and coming full circle, my life like a serpent eating its own tail, here on the Headland where it all began.